W9-BMQ-838

On-the-Job English

Workbook

Christy M. Newman

New Readers Press

On-the-Job English Workbook
ISBN 978-1-56420-250-5

Copyright © 2000 New Readers Press
New Readers Press
ProLiteracy's Publishing Division
104 Marcellus Street, Syracuse, New York 13204
www.newreaderspress.com

Printed in the United States of America
27

Proceeds from the sale of New Readers Press materials support professional development, training, and technical assistance programs of ProLiteracy that benefit local literacy programs in the U.S. and around the globe.

Director of Acquisitions and Development: Christina Jagger
Developmental Editor: Paula L. Schlusberg
Productions Director: Deborah Christiansen
Copy Editor: Julia Wittner, Judi Lauber
Design: Patricia A. Rapple
Cover Design: Kimbrly Koennecke
Illustration: Linda Tiff, Luciana Mallozzi

Contents

Lesson 1. Understanding Spoken Instructions

A. Understanding Spoken Instructions

Check ✓ the statements that give good advice about how to understand spoken instructions.

_____ 1. Always wait until your supervisor asks if you have any questions before asking them.

_____ 2. Don't worry about listening carefully the first time you hear instructions because instructions are usually repeated.

_____ 3. Repeat instructions in your own words to make sure you understand them.

_____ 4. Wait patiently until your supervisor completes all the instructions before asking any questions.

_____ 5. Be sure to remember all the instructions the first time you hear them.

_____ 6. Listen carefully the first time you get instructions.

_____ 7. Ask for additional information if a step in the instructions is not clear.

_____ 8. Don't ask too many questions, or people will think you don't know your job.

_____ 9. Listen carefully to the answers to your questions.

_____ 10. If you don't understand an instruction, you can interrupt politely and ask to hear it again.

_____ 11. Remember that most employers want you to ask questions first instead of correcting mistakes later.

_____ 12. If you don't understand your supervisor's instructions, ask a co-worker to tell you what to do.

Look at the items above that you didn't check. On another sheet, rewrite them to give good advice.

B. Asking Questions about a Job

Read the two conversations between Rae and her supervisor, Jan. Write a question for each statement.

In the Office

1. **Rae:** <u>What's my next job?</u>

   Jan: You'll remove the window screens from Building 8.

2. **Rae:** <u>When</u> _____?

   Jan: Right now. They have to be out by tonight.

3. **Rae:** <u>Why</u> _____?

   Jan: Because the windows are being washed tomorrow.

4. **Rae:** <u>Where</u> _____?

   Jan: Stack the screens in the basement of Building 8.

In Building 8

5. **Rae:** <u>Can you show me how to remove the screens?</u>

   Jan: Sure. Slide out the two holding pins from the slots in the window frame. Pull on the tabs at the sides of the screen. It'll come right out.

6. **Rae:** _____?

   Jan: Yep, those are the tabs. Then when the screen is out, put the holding pins back in their slots.

7. **Rae:** _____?

   Jan: We put them back in the slots so they don't get lost. When you're done, take the screens to the basement and stack them there.

8. **Rae:** _____?

   Jan: Good question. Show all the torn screens to the maintenance staff.

C. Following Instructions in Order

Read or listen to the conversation on page 9 of the student book. Number the pictures in correct order. Then write a sentence that describes each picture.

a.

_____

_____

c.

_____

_____

b.

_____

_____

d.

1. First, Sonia keys in the size

that she needs.

Lesson 2. Giving Spoken Instructions

A. Using Sequence Words

Put the instructions in order. Use the sequence words in the box.

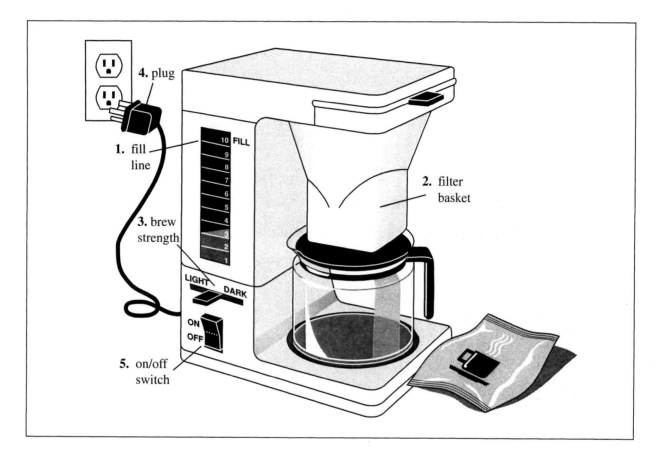

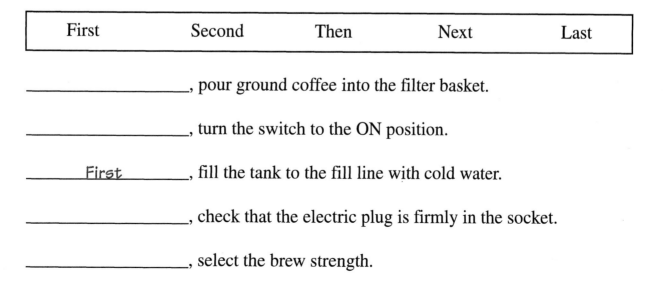

First	Second	Then	Next	Last

_____, pour ground coffee into the filter basket.

_____, turn the switch to the ON position.

_____First_____, fill the tank to the fill line with cold water.

_____, check that the electric plug is firmly in the socket.

_____, select the brew strength.

B. Giving Clear Instructions

Match each step in giving spoken instructions to a sentence that is an example.

Steps

_____ **1.** Think through the steps of a task.

_____ **2.** Explain the general purpose.

_____ **3.** Give the steps in sequence.

_____ **4.** Check that the instructions are understood.

_____ **5.** Answer questions carefully.

Examples

a. That's correct. Turn the coffee maker to ON *last*.

b. First, fill the water tank. Second, put in the coffee.

c. Everyone takes a turn making coffee first thing in the morning.

d. It's easy to do, but let me think a second, so I can tell you the right order.

e. Is that clear?

C. Giving Instructions Politely

Rewrite each statement so it is more polite or more patient.

1. I gotta teach you to use the lathe, so let's get this over with!

_____

2. That's a silly question! You don't know that?

_____

3. Pay attention! I don't want to repeat this.

_____

4. Don't you know you have to turn the engine off!

_____

5. Don't bother me. I'm too busy to explain that.

_____

6. How many times do I have to explain this to you?

_____

7. Oh, just watch what the other guys are doing. You'll catch on.

_____

8. Are you _still_ having trouble with that? Well, I guess I can go over it all again.

_____

D. Using Key Words

Use the words in the box to complete the sentences.

disconnect	wipe	faucet	handles	motor	power

1. Always lift the machine by its _____.

2. The heat comes from electric _____.

3. The water drains out when you _____ the hose.

4. The hot-water _____ is dripping.

5. Turn the key to start the _____.

6. Be sure to _____ up any paint that drips on the floor.

Lesson 3. Using Written Instructions

A. Understanding Diagrams

Use the conversation to number the diagrams in order. On another sheet, write instructions for each diagram.

Carol: My printer's out of ink. What should I do?

Inez: You have to replace the ink cartridge. Get a BI 441 cartridge from the supply closet. After you open the package, remove the yellow seal from the cartridge carefully and throw it away. Lift the printer lid and open the clamp inside. Remove the old cartridge and throw it out. Then insert the new cartridge under the clamp. Press the cartridge clamp until it clicks into place. When you close the lid, the indicator light will go on.

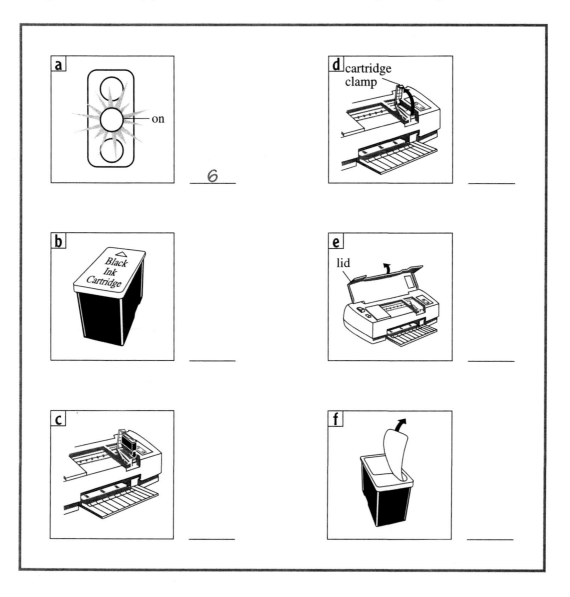

B. Interpreting a Diagram

Use the diagram to complete the directions below.

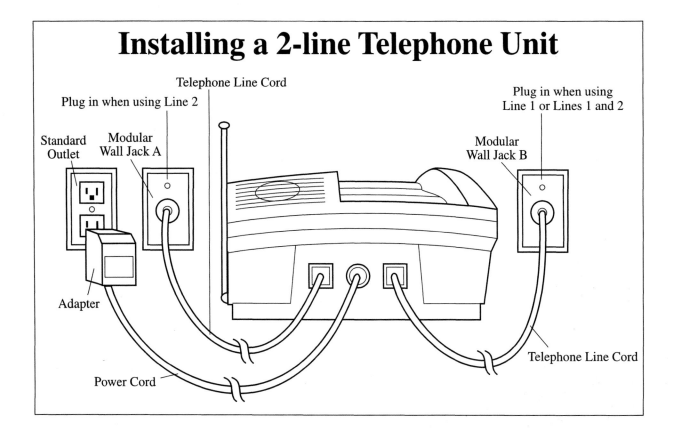

Installing a 2-line Telephone Unit

Telephone Line Cord

Plug in when using Line 2

Plug in when using
Line 1 or Lines 1 and 2

Standard
Outlet

Modular
Wall Jack A

Modular
Wall Jack B

Adapter

Telephone Line Cord

Power Cord

1. This diagram tells you _____.

2. Use a _____ cord to connect the telephone unit to a
   modular wall jack.

3. Use a _____ cord to connect the unit to a standard outlet.

4. Use wall _____ if you have only one telephone line.

5. Use an _____ plug for this unit.

6. To use telephone line ____, you can use wall jack A or B.

Lesson 4. Describing Results

A. What Did You Do?

You need to find out what work your co-worker completed during the last shift. Check ✓ the questions that can help you find out.

_____ **1.** Can you tell me what you finished?

_____ **2.** Is that all you did?

_____ **3.** Is the trim finished?

_____ **4.** Did you do more today than yesterday?

_____ **5.** Does the tank need to be refilled yet?

_____ **6.** Which part of the project still needs work?

_____ **7.** Did you order the supplies already, or should I?

B. Using Quantity Terms

Use the words in the box to complete the order.

cartons	10-lb. cans	crates	dozen	gallons	pounds

KITCHEN FRESH SUPPLIERS

Food Order for: _City Hospital Cafeteria_   Due: _5/5_

4 _____ of skim milk   2 _____ of lettuce

5 _____ of cheddar cheese   3 _____ of sliced peaches

6 _____ eggs   4 _____ of paper towels

C. Reading a Work Order

Use this work order to check ✓ the correct answers below.

GREEN THUMB NURSERY WORK ORDER

Employee: *Harry Grant*   Supervisor: *Gay Forman*

Task	Plants/Areas	Results
Water	flowers, bushes	✓
Fertilize	rows 1-4 roses rows 5-7 bulbs rows 8-10 bushes	*roses* ✓ *bulbs: row 5*
Plant in flats	35 geraniums 35 Sweet Williams 50 pansies 50 daisies	*daisies: 50 flats* *S. Will: 10 flats* *pansies: 20 flats*
Thin seedling flats	100 tomatoes 100 lettuce 100 carrots	*50 tomatoes* *50 lettuce*
Transplant to 3" pots	50 mums	*10*

Supervisor's Initials: *GF*

Harry's Tasks	Didn't Start	Partly Finished	Finished
1. water the plants			
2. fertilize the bushes			
3. fertilize the bulbs			
4. plant the daisies			
5. plant the geraniums			
6. thin the carrots			
7. transplant the mums			
8. get Gay's initials			

Lesson 5. Documenting Results

A. Interpreting Sales Records

Read these notes. Record the information in the chart. Then answer the questions.

Silver Lake Appliances

Date of Summary: *July 15*

Sales summary: Refrigerator Sales: last year and year-to-date this year

1. *Icetone freezers: last year: 388 / this year: 192*
2. *CoolJet: this yr. 75 / last yr. 98*
3. *Central Electric last yr. 422 / this year: 158*

Silver Lake Appliances

Sales data for: _____*refrigerators*_____

brand name	Last year: Jan.–Dec. 2000	Year-to-date: Jan. 1–June 30, 2001
		192
CoolJet		
	422	
totals:	*12* months, 2000	*6* months, 2001

Based on the sales so far this year:

1. Which brand sold best last year? _____

2. Which is selling better this year? _____

3. Which is selling about the same? _____

4. Will Silver Lake Appliances sell more refrigerators this year than last year?

_____.

5. The sales department wants to put Central Electric refrigerators on sale. What do you think is the reason?

_____.

B. Tallying Numbers

Yomoko uses her own car to deliver packages. She gets $.35 a mile. Complete this expense report form for Yomoko.

FLEET DELIVERY CORP.

Expense Report for Vehicle Reimbursement

Yomoko Seki			7448-9
(full name)			(employee no.)
	in	out	bi-weekly total
January 1-15	62,532	63,479	
January 16-31	63,501	65,023	
total miles			

_____ x $.35 = $_____
(total miles)   (amount owed)

Yomoko Seki   3/1/01   F.K. Wayson   3/3/01
employee   supervisor

On a separate paper, write a checklist to help Yomoko make sure her expense report is complete and accurate.

Example: _____ Are my mileage numbers accurate?

_____ Do the total miles equal the bi-weekly totals?

Lesson 6. Using Safety Gear

A. What Does It Protect?

Match the safety gear to what it protects.

_____ **1.** goggles   **a.** feet

_____ **2.** work gloves   **b.** hair

_____ **3.** work boots   **c.** clothing

_____ **4.** hard hat   **d.** face and neck

_____ **5.** respirator   **e.** back

_____ **6.** back support belt   **f.** nose, throat, and lungs

_____ **7.** headphones   **g.** eyes

_____ **8.** hairnet   **h.** head

_____ **9.** apron   **i.** ears

_____ **10.** face shield   **j.** hands

B. Safety Dress Codes

Safety gear is often required by health or safety rules. Write a reason that tells why the workers need the safety gear.

1. Carpenters must wear hard hats at construction sites.

_____

2. Lab technicians must wear rubber gloves.

_____

3. Kitchen workers should wear hairnets.

_____

4. Auto mechanics have to wear rubber-soled shoes.

_____

5. OSHA says floor sanders must use earplugs.

_____

C. The Right Equipment for the Job

Match the people at work to the equipment they need to work safely. Add an example of your own.

_____ **1.** Computer programmers often wear

_____ **2.** OSHA says welders need

_____ **3.** Electricians usually wear

_____ **4.** When gardeners use electric saws to trim hedges or cut branches they should wear

_____ **5.** To prevent lower back strain, movers often wear

_____ **6.** When they're removing hot items from the oven, bakers should use

_____ **7.** Housekeepers who use harsh chemical cleaners should wear

_____ **8.** Cashiers who stand all day often have

_____ **9.** Because they sit all day, telephone operators need

_____ **10.** _____

_____

a. headphones to protect their hearing.

b. work shoes with rubber soles to avoid shocks.

c. good chairs that support the back.

d. wrist braces to avoid problems with repetitive-motion tasks.

e. thick rubber gloves to avoid skin irritation.

f. cushioned mats to protect their feet.

g. fireproof face shields to protect them from flying sparks.

h. back support braces when they lift furniture.

i. heatproof mitts so their hands and fingers don't get burned.

j. _____

_____

D. What's Wrong Here?

Write a sentence that describes the problem in each picture.
Use the words in the box to help.

butcher/rubber gloves	construction worker/hard hat
carpenter/face shield	cook/hairnet

1.

_____

_____

3.

_____

_____

2.

_____

_____

4.

_____

_____

Lesson 7. Understanding Rules and Regulations

A. Following Safety Rules

Read the safety rules. On separate paper, write a reason for each rule. Then use the rules to complete the exercise below.

SAFETY RULES AT SELECT MANUFACTURING CO.

1. Goggles and headphones must be worn at all times on factory floors.
2. Keep emergency doors unlocked and unblocked.
3. Clean up spills immediately.
4. Report accidents and injuries immediately.
5. Smoking is not allowed in any Select buildings.
6. Close all containers of chemicals and store in cabinet when not in use.

Read the situations. For each one, write what rule was broken.

_____ **a.** When Mr. Gray smokes in his office, he opens a window.

_____ **b.** Maury got a sliver of glass in his hand. After he finished his shift, he reported the injury.

_____ **c.** Alia stored empty cartons near an exit door so the cleaning staff could remove them.

_____ **d.** Frank was in a hurry, so he left an open bottle of turpentine on the floor near his work station.

_____ **e.** The water that drips from my water bottle dries quickly, so I don't bother to wipe it up.

_____ **f.** Most of the machines were off yesterday, so we didn't need to use headphones.

B. Safe or Unsafe

Check ✓ if the situation is safe or unsafe.

	Safe	Unsafe
1. The first-aid kit is in some drawer in the office.		
2. Li wears safety gear when he turns on his machine.		
3. Kim lifts heavy packages without bending her knees.		
4. The maintenance workers wear beepers so they can get to accidents quickly.		
5. My boss checks the smoke detectors every month.		
6. Ray checks all safety gear before he puts it away.		
7. The emergency exits are locked after eight o'clock so that nobody will bother the night shift.		
8. Empty chemical containers are removed quickly from work areas by a biohazard crew.		
9. Alfredo is getting new goggles soon. He doesn't use his old ones because they don't fit well.		

Look at the statements you checked "Unsafe." On a separate paper, rewrite them to describe a safe situation.

C. Using Key Words

Complete the sentences with words in the box.

alarm pull	first-aid kit	safety glasses	fire extinguisher

1. Carpenters need _____ at the table saw.

2. Every _____ contains antiseptic cream and bandages.

3. Use the _____ to warn of danger.

4. Keep a _____ in the cafeteria.

Lesson 8. Following Safety Rules

A. Understanding Warning Signs

Match each statement to the appropriate warning sign.
Some signs will be used more than once.

_____ 1. The machines make so much noise!

_____ 2. I smell smoke!

_____ 3. The maintenance crew finished cleaning up the spill.

_____ 4. That's the circuit room for the building.

_____ 5. It's so strong even the fumes can make you sick.

_____ 6. That grill's been on all day.

_____ 7. Bricks or dirt might fall from the fork lift.

_____ 8. We're not allowed to eat near the machines.

_____ 9. You'll be working at the rock concert here next week.

_____ 10. They just washed the floor in the break room.

_____ 11. Don't put that in the refrigerator! It's poison!

_____ 12. We need to visit the construction site today.

_____ 13. Watch out! That pipe carried live steam!

_____ 14. We can't have any food spills in the lab.

B. Safety First!

Write a sentence that tells what can happen if you don't follow the safety guideline.

1. Do not clean fan blades with your hands or cleaning objects while the fan is plugged in.

You might cut your fingers.

2. Don't repair or open power tools while the current is on.

_____

3. Use a dust mask at all times when sanding floors.

_____

4. Keep hands and feet inside moving vehicles.

_____

5. Wear a helmet when you drive the forklift.

_____

6. Wipe up spills immediately.

_____

7. Call the cleaning crew to remove broken glass. Don't do it yourself.

_____

8. Leave the vent fan on in the lab at all times.

_____

9. When you work at a computer, get up and stretch once an hour.

_____

Lesson 9. Safety Problems at Work

A. What Would You Do?

Imagine you are the supervisor. Describe what you would do for each problem.

1. **Problem:** A fluorescent light tube snapped while Matt was changing it. The broken glass cut his hand, and it is bleeding a lot.

   Supervisor: _I would give Matt a clean cloth to press on the cut. Then I'd_

   call an ambulance.

2. **Problem:** The temperature in the cafeteria kitchen is over 80°.

   Supervisor: _____

   _____

3. **Problem:** It is raining outside. Puddles of water have dripped from shoes and umbrellas in the front hall.

   Supervisor: _____

   _____

4. **Problem:** The boss wants to show a friend around the machine shop. The friend is wearing high heels, a long scarf, and designer sunglasses.

   Supervisor: _____

   _____

5. **Problem:** The emergency gasoline can is leaking.

   Supervisor: _____

   _____

B. Filling Out an Accident Report Form

Read the story. Then complete the accident report form.

Matt Winslow was changing a fluorescent light in Ellen Towner's office at 4:15 on Thursday afternoon. The light tube snapped as Matt put it in the fixture. The broken glass cut his left hand. It started bleeding. Ellen saw the accident and called Matt's supervisor, Aaron Fisher. Aaron rushed in with a first-aid kit. He gave Matt a sterile pad to hold against the cut, which kept bleeding. Aaron took Matt to Hopedale Clinic. The emergency room doctor cleaned the cut and closed it with nine stitches. She also gave Matt a tetanus shot. Aaron drove Matt home. When Aaron returned to work, he filed an accident report.

SACKS GLASS WORKS, INC.

Injury Report

Please complete this report within 24 hours of accident and file it with the Insurance Records Department.

Person(s) hurt: _____

Location of accident: _____ at 554 Low St., Hopedale

Time of accident: _____ am _____ pm

Date of accident: _9/29/01_____

Describe the accident: _____

_____

_____

Treated at: _____

by: _Roberta Lender, M.D._____

Witness(es) to the event: _____

Name and position of person filing this report:

_____

Lesson 10. Understanding Roles and Responsibilities

A. Reading an Organizational Chart

Use the finance department chart to complete the sentences below.

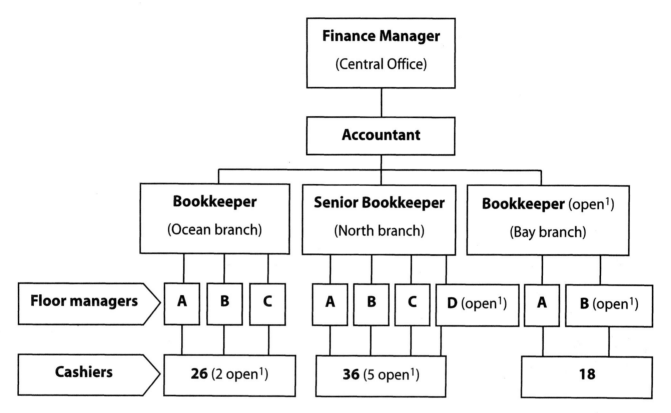

1 "Open" means there is a job opening.

1. Ocean, North, and Bay are _____ stores.

2. The accountant works in the _____ office with the finance manager.

3. Bookkeepers usually _____ report to the finance manager.

4. Floor managers report to _____.

5. A floor manager supervises about _____ cashiers.

6. Together, the branch stores need _____ more floor managers.

7. North branch needs _____ more cashiers.

B. Using an Organizational Chart

Read the statements below. Explain why you agree or disagree with each decision. Use the chart on page 25 to help you decide.

1. The Bay branch floor manager thinks he should report to the senior bookkeeper at the North branch.

   I agree. There's no bookkeeper at Bay, and it makes sense that the

   senior bookkeeper would fill in.

2. A cashier finds her tally at the Ocean branch is wrong. She decides to talk to Ocean's bookkeeper.

   _____

   _____

3. The accountant is interviewing Enid Gates for the bookkeeper job. The accountant wants the other bookkeepers to interview her also.

   _____

   _____

4. The finance manager is reviewing staff problems. She meets with the floor managers about staffing needs.

   _____

   _____

5. Tina is a cashier at the Ocean store. She has completed all the bookkeeping courses at night school. Tina calls the accountant in central office to apply for the bookkeeping job.

   _____

   _____

C. Using Two-Word Verbs

Complete the dialogs with these two-word verbs.

check off	gives out	pull down
put on	open up	turn off

1. **Cindy:** Do I have to _____ (wear) all this safety gear?

2. **Paolo:** You should use everything the company _____ (distributes).

3. **Hank:** Excuse me. How do I _____ (unfold) the table legs?

4. **Ben:** First, press that hinge, then _____ (lower) one leg at a time.

5. **Terry:** Can you help me _____ (stop) the machines?

6. **Fred:** Sure. Just let me _____ (record) my completed work order first.

D. Writing a Description

**Describe the roles and responsibilities of people at your workplace.
Use the organizational chart you made on page 71 of the student book.**

_____

_____

_____

_____

_____

_____

Lesson 11. Asking for and Offering Help

A. Asking for Help/Offering Help

Check ✓ the clear, short, and polite ways of asking for help.

_____ **1.** Excuse me. Could you help me change this tape?

_____ **2.** Would you mind giving me a hand moving this box?

_____ **3.** Help me sharpen this blade, OK?

_____ **4.** I'm sorry to interrupt, but I'm not sure how to put this bolt back, and I have to move this machine right away. Can you help?

_____ **5.** Pardon me, would you mind holding this ladder?

Check ✓ the clear and polite ways of offering help.

_____ **6.** Please let me show you how to change the tape.

_____ **7.** You can't lift that box by yourself!

_____ **8.** I'll be happy to show you how to use the tool sharpener.

_____ **9.** Is there a problem? Maybe I can help.

_____ **10.** Hey, someone should hold that ladder for you.

On another sheet, rewrite the statements that you didn't check so they ask for or offer help in a better way.

B. Responding Politely

Rewrite the underlined responses to make them more polite.

1. Could you please tell me where I can store my tools?
   <u>Yeah. Follow me.</u>

   _____

2. I'm supposed to get files for my boss, but there aren't any in the supply closet. What should I do?
   <u>Good grief! Just call down to the stock room!</u>

   _____

3. Excuse me. How do I get to the employees' parking lot?
<u>Didn't you see the signs in the locker room?</u>

_____

4. Should I deliver these packages now, or wait until the mail is ready, too?
<u>Now why would you waste your time making two trips?</u>

_____

C. Clear Requests

Rewrite these requests. Make them clear, short, and polite.

1. I should know how to use this fax machine already, but would
you show me again? My boss showed me how to use it last week,
but I haven't used it since then, and now I have to fax this letter
to a customer.

_____

2. Aldo is new here today, and he's supposed to work with me all
day, but I have to go to the branch store for an hour. I don't think
he should come with me, so could you work with him while
I'm gone?

_____

3. You know I usually work from noon to eight on Monday nights,
but my daughter is in the school play, and I'd really like to see it.
Can you trade shifts with me just for this one Monday so I can
go to her play?

_____

Lesson 12. Expressing Opinions

A. Giving Opinions Effectively

Match the advice about giving opinions to a sentence that is an example.

Advice

_____ 1. It's OK to disagree with someone if you do it politely.

_____ 2. It's a good idea to give reasons for your opinion.

_____ 3. You should listen carefully to other people's opinions.

_____ 4. Comment on an idea, not on a person.

_____ 5. Try to find a solution that everyone can support.

Examples

a. I think that will work well because it means we can meet the deadline.

b. Now I understand what you mean. Thanks for explaining that.

c. Can we all agree with that plan of action?

d. Excuse me, but I don't think that solves the problem.

e. I really like Bob's idea for adjusting this process.

B. Polite Interactions at Work

Check ✓ the polite ways to give an opinion.

_____ 1. What do you think about this idea?

_____ 2. My suggestion is still the only way to go.

_____ 3. How about looking at it from this point of view?

_____ 4. I think we could do it like this.

_____ 5. That won't work. Here's what we should do.

Check ✓ the polite ways to disagree.

_____ 6. That's ridiculous. I'd never do it that way!

_____ 7. I'm sorry, but it doesn't seem to work.

_____ 8. The idea is good, but it's too expensive.

_____ 9. No way! You're completely off base.

_____ 10. I'm afraid we need a different solution.

C. A Better Way to Say It

Rewrite the sentences to make them polite *and* assertive.

1. You can't make me do it like that. My way is right.

_____

2. I don't care. I'll go along with whatever you decide.

_____

3. It's not fair. Why should my team do all the work?

_____

4. No way! You don't know what you're talking about!

_____

5. Well . . . , I'll do it if you say so.

_____

6. I guess that's OK. I'll do it your way.

_____

7. These numbers can't be right. Did you double-check?

_____

8. I'm new here, so I'd rather not say what I think.

_____

9. It's obvious that this is the only good way to do the job.

_____

Lesson 13. Giving and Getting Feedback

A. Responding to an Evaluation

At Beth's last performance evaluation, her supervisor told her she wasn't ready for a promotion. Check ✓ what Beth can say.

_____ **1.** I'm going to try harder next time.

_____ **2.** You don't know what you're talking about.

_____ **3.** I can do better if you give me another chance.

_____ **4.** Maybe I need to review my work plan again.

_____ **5.** I'd like to show you how much better I can do.

_____ **6.** You never liked me.

_____ **7.** Oh? Did you give the promotion to your friend?

_____ **8.** I think I could use some advice on how to improve.

B. Responding to Feedback

Read the situations and the supervisor's feedback. Then complete the conversations.

1. Lina takes care of the supply closet. It's very messy. Items are not in the correct boxes. Some boxes are empty and supplies need to be ordered.

Supervisor: Lina, I can't find the office supplies I need. You need to spend some time organizing this closet. We're low on some supplies, too.

Lina: _____

2. Mark is never more than 15 minutes late for work. But this month, he was late five times.

Supervisor: You're a good worker, Mark, but your lateness is a serious problem. What can you do to get here on time?

Mark: _____

C. Interpreting Performance Evaluations

Read the evaluation. Then use the information to complete the sentences.

6-Month Probation Review

(to be completed by supervisor)

Name: *Leah Strand* **Position:** *Cashier*

This employee:	(check ✓ one)		
knows the job	excellent	✓good	poor
can correct errors	excellent	✓good	poor
works with customers	excellent	✓good	poor
shows initiative	✓excellent	good	poor
uses feedback to improve	excellent	✓good	poor
neat appearance	excellent	good	✓poor
maintains uniform	excellent	good	✓poor
was late 4 times	was absent O days		

Strengths: *friendly, out-going, asks questions; does extra work; learns from mistakes, o.k. with customers.*

Areas for improvement: *needs to get to work on time; sometimes has careless appearance & a wrinkled uniform.*

Recommendation: *end probation/continue training*

---

1. Leah works as a _____.

2. She is best at _____.

3. She needs to improve _____.

4. She also has to _____.

5. She was never _____.

6. Her supervisor thinks Leah _____.

7. I think Leah _____.

Lesson 14. Following Schedules

A. Understanding Work Schedules

Mary is a home healthcare aide. Use the note from her supervisor to fill in her date book. Then complete the exercise below.

Dear Mary:

Here's your work schedule for this week. The staff meeting is on Friday 8–9 am

Ms. Grand: Mon. 8–10; Wed. 11–3

Mr. Wyatt: Mon. 11–1; Thurs. 12–2; Fri. 10–12

Ms. Forest: Tues. 11–2; Thurs. 8–11

Ms. Brown: Mon. 2–4; Tues. 8–10; Fri. 2–4

time	Monday	Tuesday	Wednesday	Thursday	Friday
8:00					
9:00					
10:00					
11:00					
12:00					
1:00					
2:00					
3:00					
4:00					

	True	False
1. Mary has more than 3 patients a day.		
2. The longest session is 4 hours long.		
3. She sees patients only once a week.		
4. Mary could go to the staff meeting if it was moved to Thursday from 3 to 4 P.M.		
5. She sees a patient before Mr. Wyatt on Friday.		

B. Changing Work Schedules

Complete the conversations. Give a good reason for each request.

1. **Supervisor:** Good morning, Ana Perez speaking.

   Alban: Hi, Ana. This is Alban. I'm going to be late this morning.
   I won't be in until eleven because

   _____

   _____

2. **Supervisor:** Why do you want the night shift next week?

   Li Ho: I'd like to trade and work the night shift so

   _____

   _____

3. **Supervisor:** What can I do for you?

   Fred: I need to take a personal day on Friday because

   _____

   _____

4. **Supervisor:** What did you want to see me about, Myra?

   Myra: Would it be OK if I came in late tomorrow because

   _____

   _____

5. **Supervisor:** This is Ray speaking. How can I help you?

   Tony: Hi, Ray. I can't come to work today because

   _____

   _____

Lesson 15. Understanding Announcements

A. Using Abbreviations in Announcements

Read the announcements. Complete each one with abbreviations in the box.

a/c = air conditioning	gd. = good	p/t = part time
apt. = apartment	hr. = hour	pls = please
exp'd = experienced	mo. = month	refs. = references
ext. = telephone extension	no. = north	Rd. = road

a. New employees: _____ turn in your completed Form W-4s before you report to work. Questions? Call Rico at _____ 6644

b. Center City Rental: 4-rm _____. 1 br, clean, sunny kit. partly furn. near pub. transp. $500/ _____ + deposit. Ray X879

c. FREE! cuddly kittens and pups. Brookline Animal Shelter 1 mile _____ of town center at 22 Center _____. Call: PET-PUPS (738-7877)

d. _____ handyperson. Can do all home repairs. No job too small. Local _____ avail. Margie 555-0909

e. admin asst. needed: _____ 16 hrs/wk: M-T-W-T 1-5pm. Basic wd. proc. skills. Gd. phone manner. $9.50/_____ Conv. loc. nr. Haven Mall. 555-0007.

f. For sale: '99 Accord wagon; black, 42K; _____ cond., 5-spd. nu tires. am/fm cass., _____ $9,950/BO. call Harry x3289

B. Finding Useful Announcements

Read the situations. Pick an announcement from page 36 that
each person should read. Then explain why you think the
announcement can be useful to that person.

_f_ **1.** Marc's wife is having a baby.

They will need a bigger car for the baby's car seat. A station wagon will

be useful as the baby grows up.

_____ **2.** Anton needs a part-time job.

_____

_____ **3.** Mahmoud wants to get his son a birthday present.

_____

_____ **4.** Rosanna starts work in two days.

_____

C. Writing Announcements

Read the situations. On index cards or on separate paper, create
a bulletin board announcement for each one. Use abbreviations
and add any information that you think is important.

1. Paul's daughter is selling Girl Scout cookies. Paul is taking orders
   from people at work.

2. Gina is selling her car. It is a 4-door, 1999 blue Ford Taurus with
   air conditioning, automatic transmission, and an am/fm cassette
   player. It has 45,000 miles, and she wants to get at least $8,000.

3. The employee daycare center has an opening for a 2-year-old in
   the toddler classroom.

4. The company wants everyone who does heavy lifting to wear a
   back support belt. Belts can be purchased at cost from the safety
   equipment department.

Lesson 16. Job Postings

A. Using Job Postings

Which jobs fit Hanna's and Pedro's needs and skills? Write two
job titles and phone numbers for each employee.

Toasty Bread Co. Seeks 3 bakers to join the crew at Greenfield's best bakery. Flex. schedules. Exp. or cooking school diploma req. $9/hr. med/dent/ retirement 990-8732	**Reservations Clerk** Computer literate, outgoing people needed for our winning team. Competitive salary/job training/ good benefits/pd vacations. ft/pt Thrifty Moving Rentals 444-0909
Machine Operator clothing manufacturer. Must have good basic math skills. no exp. nec. good pay/flex. hours/benefits. near public transp. Cotton Wear Co. 990-7762	**Newspaper Delivery Person** adults (18+) w/ driver's license and dependable transportation to deliver newspapers around city. Daily or weekends: early mornings. $8-11/hr. plus bonuses. Call Jane at 808-555-1212 Community Newspaper, Inc.

1. Hanna measured and cut dress patterns in her last job. She knows
   word processing and loves to cook. She can work while her children
   are in school. She needs medical and dental benefits and wants to
   work for a big company.

   Hanna can be a _____. She should call _____.
   OR
   She can be a _____. She should call _____.

2. Pedro is starting a computer training program that meets from
   noon to 6 P.M. every weekday. He can work mornings, evenings
   after 7 P.M., or weekends. He drives a pickup truck and likes working
   with people. He was a cook in his native country and speaks Spanish
   and English.

   Pedro can be a _____. He should call _____.
   OR
   He can be a _____. He should call _____.

B. Learning More about Jobs

Pick one of the jobs on page 38 for Hanna and one for Pedro.
Write two questions they can ask to learn more about those jobs.

1. Hanna wants to be _____. To learn more about the job, she can ask:

   _____?

   _____?

2. Pedro wants to be _____. To learn more about the job, he can ask:

   _____?

   _____?

C. Understanding a Job Posting

Read the posting and answer the questions.

JOB OPENINGS

Hosts/Hostesses/Food Servers

Great opportunities in our busy winter season for professional, full-time restaurant workers.

Team-oriented people with 1–2 years' experience in fast-paced workplace should apply in person at 23 Spark St.

---

1. What kind of company posted this ad? _____

2. What kind of worker is the company looking for? _____

3. What qualifications are required?

   _____

Lesson 17. Reading Memos

A. Understanding Memos

Write a subject for each memo. Use the information in the
memos to check ✓ the right answer in the exercise below.

a.
TO: Best Wear employees
FROM: Security
RE: _____

After 8 pm, please enter and exit
the building through the main lobby.
All other doors will be locked until
6 am.

c.
TO: All employees
FROM: Payroll
RE: _____

If you wish to change your health
insurance plan, please complete the
attached forms. Return them to the
Payroll Department NO LATER than
Friday, April 15 at noon.

b.
TO: Sales staff
FROM: Sales supervisor
RE: _____

New returns policy: Without a
receipt, we allow only exchange or
in-store credit. With a receipt, continue
to issue a full credit for up to 30 days.

d.
TO: Data Entry clerks
FROM: Mr. Bowman
RE: _____

Our department has arranged for
advanced computer training through
Highbridge Community College.
Tuition will be paid directly by Best
Wear. Register in my office by 4/9.

1. Alva works from midnight to 8 A.M. She
   ____ must leave through the main lobby   ____ can use any exit

2. The new returns policy is for customers
   ____ with receipts   ____ without receipts

3. You can make health plan changes
   ____ before April 15   ____ after April 15

4. Registration for the advanced computer course is at
   ____ Highbridge Community College   ____ Best Wear Company

B. Figuring Percentages

Best Wear Company pays part of its workers' benefits. Each worker pays the rest. Complete the chart.

Benefit	Best Wear	Worker
Workers' Compensation	100 %	-0-
Medical (pick one)		
• Community Health		
individual plan	____%	25%
family plan	60%	____%
• HealthWise		
individual plan only	90%	____%
Dental (optional)	15%	____%
Retirement	____%	30%

Use the information from the chart. Check ✓ true, false or NI (not enough information).

Workers at Best Wear	True	False	NI
1. get free Workers' Compensation.			
2. get two health plans.			
3. can pick individual or family health plans.			
4. think HealthWise is a better medical plan for single workers.			
5. have to pay for dental insurance.			
6. can retire at 62.			

Lesson 18. Taking Telephone Messages

A. A Good First Impression

Check ✓ good ways to answer the phone at work.

_____ **1.** Crossroads Takeout. May I take your order?

_____ **2.** Hi. Who's this?

_____ **3.** Hold on a second. I'll be right with you.

_____ **4.** This is Marty. Leave a message at the beep.

_____ **5.** Good afternoon, front desk. How may I help you?

_____ **6.** Walker Corporation. How may I direct your call?

_____ **7.** Art department. This is Sonia speaking.

_____ **8.** Yeah? Who're you trying to reach?

Look at the statements you didn't check. On separate paper, rewrite them to provide better ways to answer a work phone.

B. Speaking Politely on the Phone

Read these statements from workplace telephone operators. Check ✓ the ones you think are appropriate. On a separate paper, rewrite the ones you did not check.

_____ **1.** Mr. Walker will get your message as soon as he returns.

_____ **2.** Hey, slow down, lady! What was that name again?

_____ **3.** I think Alphonse is at extension 76. Why don't you try calling him there?

_____ **4.** Ms. Freeman is out sick. I think she has the flu. It's going around the office.

_____ **5.** Could you repeat your phone number, so I can make sure I have it down right?

_____ **6.** Good-bye, and thank you for calling Quality Paper.

C. Writing Out Messages

Read the message left on the answering machine. Complete the message form.

"Hi. This is Gwen Wilder. I'm trying to reach Fred because I have to change my flight to Chicago. Please have him call me right back. I'm at the bookstore."

```
┌─────────────────────────────────────────────────────────┐
│                    IMPORTANT MESSAGE                      │
│  _____  │
│                                                          │
│   TO:  _____ │
│                                                          │
│   FROM: _____ │
│                                                          │
│   COMPANY: _____ │
│                                                          │
│   PHONE: (_____)_____ │
│                                                          │
│   _____ please call back    _____ returned your call │
│                                                          │
│   _____ URGENT              _____ will call back │
│                                                          │
│   MESSAGE: _____ │
│                                                          │
│   _____ │
│                                                          │
└─────────────────────────────────────────────────────────┘
```

Write questions you would have asked Gwen if you had answered this call.

1. <u>What is your telephone number</u> _____?

2. _____?

3. _____?

4. _____?

Answer Key

Unit 1

Lesson 1

A. Understanding Spoken Instructions (p. 4)

Check 3, 6, 7, 9, 10, 11

B. Asking Questions about a Job (p. 5)

Possible answers:

2. When should I start?

3. Why do they need to be removed?

4. Where should I put the screens?

6. Are these the tabs?

7. Why do we put the pins back in the slots?

8. What if the screens are damaged?

C. Following Instructions in Order (p. 6)

a. 2, b. 4, c. 3. Sentences will vary.

Lesson 2

A. Using Sequence Words (p. 7)

Second, Last, First, Next, Then, OR

Second, Last, First, Then, Next

B. Giving Clear Instructions (p. 8)

1. d, 2. c, 3. b, 4. e, 5. a

C. Giving Instructions Politely (p. 8)

Answers will vary.

D. Using Key Words (p. 9)

1. handles, 2. power, 3. disconnect, 4. faucet, 5. motor, 6. wipe

Lesson 3

A. Understanding Diagrams (p. 10)

b. 1, c. 5, d. 4, e. 3, f. 2

Instructions will vary.

B. Interpreting a Diagram (p. 11)

1. how to install a 2-line telephone unit, 2 telephone line, 3. power, 4. jack B, 5. adapter, 6. 2

Lesson 4

A. What Did You Do? (p. 12)

Check 1, 3, 5, 6, 7

B. Using Quantity Terms (p. 12)

4 **gallons** of skim milk

5 **pounds** of cheddar cheese

6 **dozen** eggs

2 **crates** of lettuce

3 **10-lb. cans** of sliced peaches

4 **cartons** of paper towels

C. Reading a Work Order (p. 13)

1. Finished	5. Didn't Start
2. Didn't Start	6. Didn't Start
3. Partly Finished	7. Partly Finished
4. Finished	8. Finished

Lesson 5

A. Interpreting Sales Records (p. 14)

Silver Lake Appliances

Sales data for: _refrigerators_

brand name	Last year Jan-Dec. 2000	Year-to-date: Jan 1-June 30, 2001
Icetone	388	192
CoolJet	98	75
Central Electric	422	158
totals:	12 months, 2000 908	6 months, 2001 425

1. Central Electric

2. CoolJet

3. Icetone

4. Probably not. You may guess sales for the whole year will be 850 since they were 425 for the first half. Last year's sales were 908.

5. Possible answer: Central Electric isn't selling as well this year as last year.

B. Tallying Numbers (p. 15)

	in	out	bi-weekly total
January 1-15	62,532	63,479	947 miles
January 16-31	63,501	65,023	1522 miles
total miles			2469 miles

2469 miles x $.35 = $ _$864.15_
(total miles)　　　　　　　　(amount owed)

Checklists will vary.

Unit 2

Lesson 6

A. What Does It Protect? (p. 16)

1. g, 2. j, 3. a, 4. h, 5. f, 6. e, 7. i, 8. b, 9. c, 10. d

B. Safety Dress Codes (p. 16)

Possible reasons:

1. to protect their heads from falling objects

2. so they won't get infections

3. so their hair doesn't get caught in machines

4. because garage floors are oily and slippery

5. to protect their ears from the noise

C. The Right Equipment for the Job (p. 17)

1. d, 2. g, 3. b, 4. a, 5. h, 6. i, 7. e, 8. f, 9. c

D. What's Wrong Here? (p. 18)

Answers will vary.

▮ Lesson 7

A. Following Safety Rules (p. 19)

Possible reasons:

1. to protect eyes and ears from the machines
2. so that it's easy to escape in an emergency
3. to keep workers from slipping and falling
4. so that injuries can be taken care of quickly
5. to prevent fires
6. to protect workers from toxic fumes and to prevent chemical spills

a. 5, b. 4, c. 2, d. 6, e. 3, f. 1

B. Safe or Unsafe (p. 20)

1. Unsafe, 2. Safe, 3. Unsafe, 4. Safe, 5. Safe, 6. Safe, 7. Unsafe, 8. Safe, 9. Unsafe

C. Using Key Words (p. 20)

1. safety glasses
2. first-aid kit
3. alarm pull
4. fire extinguisher

▮ Lesson 8

A. Understanding Warning Signs (p. 21)

1. d, 2. g, 3. a, 4. f, 5. b, 6. c, 7. h, 8. e, 9. d, 10. a, 11. b, 12. h, 13. c, 14. e

B. Safety First! (p. 22)

Answers will vary.

▮ Lesson 9

A. What Would You Do? (p. 23)

Answers will vary.

B. Filling Out an Accident Report Form (p. 24)

SACKS GLASS WORKS, INC.

Injury Report

Please complete this report within 24 hours of accident and file it with the Insurance Records Department.

Person(s) hurt: _Matt Winslow_

Location of accident: _Sacks Glass Works, Inc. at 554 Low St., Hopedale_

Time of accident: _____ am _4:15_ pm

Date of accident: _9/29/01_

Describe the accident: _Matt was changing a light fixture which broke and cut his left hand. I gave him first aid on site and then drove him to the emergency room. The doctor cleaned the wound and put in 9 stitches._

Treated at: _Hopedale Clinic - Emergency Room_

by: _Roberta Lender, M.D._

Witness(es) to the event: _Ellen Towner_

Name and position of person filing this report: _Aaron Fisher, supervisor_

Unit 3

▮ Lesson 10

A. Reading an Organizational Chart (p. 25)

1. branch
2. central
3. don't
4. bookkeepers
5. 9
6. 2
7. 5

B. Using an Organizational Chart (p. 26)

Possible answers:

2. I disagree. The cashier should talk to her floor manager.
3. I agree. Sometimes workers have good ideas about applicants they will have to work with.
4. I agree. It's a good idea for the finance manager to find out their needs and ideas directly from the people she supervises.
5. I disagree. Tina should call the personnel office to apply for a job.

C. Using Two-Word Verbs (p. 27)

1. put on, 2. gives out, 3. open up, 4. pull down, 5. turn off, 6. check off

D. Writing a Description (p. 27)

Answers will vary.

▮ Lesson 11

A. Asking for Help/Offering Help (p. 28)

Check 1, 2, 5, 6, 8, 9

B. Responding Politely (p. 28)

Answers will vary.

C. Clear Requests (p. 29)

Possible answers:

1. Pardon me. Could you please show me how to use the fax machine again?
2. Excuse me. Would you mind working with my trainee, Aldo, for about an hour while I go to the branch store?
3. I'm trying to change my Monday noon to eight shift. Could I trade with you?

▮ Lesson 12

A. Giving Opinions Effectively (p. 30)

1. d, 2. a, 3. b, 4. e, 5. c

B. Polite Interactions at Work (p. 30)

Check 1, 3, 4, 7, 8, 10

C. A Better Way to Say It (p. 31)

Answers will vary.

Lesson 13

A. Responding to an Evaluation (p. 32)

Check 1, 3, 4, 5, 8

B. Responding to Feedback (p. 32)

Answers will vary.

C. Interpreting Performance Evaluations (p. 33)

1. cashier
2. showing initiative
3. her appearance
4. maintain her uniform better
5. absent
6–7. Answers will vary.

Unit 4

Lesson 14

A. Understanding Work Schedules (p. 34)

time	Monday	Tuesday	Wednesday	Thursday	Friday
8:00	Grand ↓	Brown ↓		Forest	staff
9:00					
10:00				↓	Wyatt
11:00	Wyatt	Forest	Grand		↓
12:00	↓			Wyatt	
1:00		↓		↓	
2:00	Brown		↓		Brown
3:00	↓				↓
4:00					

1. False, 2. True, 3. False, 4. True, 5. False

B. Changing Work Schedules (p. 35)

Answers will vary.

Lesson 15

A. Using Abbreviations in Announcements (p. 36)

a. pls, ext. d. exp'd, refs.
b. apt., mo. e. p/t, hr.
c. no., Rd. f. gd., a/c

B. Finding Useful Announcements (p. 37)

2. e, 3. c, 4. a. Explanations will vary.

C. Writing Announcements (p. 37)

Answers will vary.

Lesson 16

A. Using Job Postings (p. 38)

1. reservations clerk/444-0909, OR
   machine operator/990-7762

2. baker/990-8732, OR
   newspaper delivery person/808-555-1212

B. Learning More about Jobs (p. 39)

Answers will vary.

C. Understanding a Job Posting (p. 39)

1. a restaurant
2. professional, team-oriented
3. 1–2 years' experience

Lesson 17

A. Understanding Memos (p. 40)

Subjects will vary.

1. can use any exit
2. without receipts
3. before April 15
4. Best Wear Company

B. Figuring Percentages (p. 41)

Benefit	Best Wear	Worker
Workers' Compensation	100%	-0-
Medical (pick one)		
• Community Health		
individual plan	75%	25%
family plan	60%	40%
• HealthWise		
individual plan only	90%	10%
Dental (optional)	15%	85%
Retirement	70%	30%

1. true, 2. false, 3. true, 4. NI, 5. false, 6. NI

Lesson 18

A. A Good First Impression (p. 42)

Check 1, 5, 6, 7

B. Speaking Politely on the Phone (p. 42)

Check 1, 5, 6

C. Writing Out Messages (p. 43)

```
                IMPORTANT MESSAGE

  TO:        Fred
  FROM:      Gwen Wilder
  COMPANY:
  PHONE: (        )
   ✓  please call back          _____ returned your call
   ✓  URGENT                    _____ will call back
  MESSAGE:   She has to change her flight to Chicago.
   She's at the bookstore.
```

Questions will vary.

Teacher's Notes

The goal of these notes is to provide useful hints for using the activities in this workbook to develop students' workplace language skills. The workbook activities are designed to reinforce, review, or expand the objectives of the *On-the-Job English* student book. Students can work independently or in pairs or groups. Activities are grouped below by type. For each type there is a listing of the activities of that type in the workbook, a brief description of the activity's purpose, and a set of ideas to expand the exercises and to make them relevant to an individual's workplace.

1. **Vocabulary/Grammar** (2A, 2D, 4B, 6A, 6B, 7C, 10A, 10C): These exercises reinforce vocabulary and/or grammar structures, primarily through readings or cloze activities that reinforce sequence, quantity, or key vocabulary.

   Expansions:

   • Have students keep individual vocabulary dictionaries. They can include key words from each unit and add similar key words from their own workplaces. Then individually or in pairs they can categorize groups of words in their dictionaries (e.g., by type of workplace or kinds of safety equipment).

   • Have students scan work memos, instructions, or newspaper and magazine articles for examples of grammar, such as two-word verbs, practiced in a lesson.

2. **Matching** (2B, 6A, 6C, 7A, 8A, 12A): These activities reinforce understanding by eliciting pairs of concepts/advice/rules/signs and concrete examples or expressions.

   Expansions:

   • Have students brainstorm a list of equipment they use at their workplace and let others figure out a matching use.

   • Have students write examples of inappropriate expressions they've heard at their workplace (e.g., instructions, requests, phone comments) and let others write a better way of saying the same thing.

• When students learn the names of people in the class, they can create activities that match them to their jobs, native countries, places of employment, equipment they use, etc.

• Give students a list of generic places of business (bakery, machine shop, hotel, etc.). Students then come up with a parallel list of matches in categories such as products, equipment, main tasks, service, etc. Finally, have students share their matches.

• Have students use a given matching exercise as a model to create a parallel version using examples from their own workplace.

3. **Cloze** (2A, 3B, 10A, 15A, 16A): These fill-in exercises reinforce comprehension skills. Information for fill-ins may be presented in a word box, a diagram, or a reading.

   Expansions:

   • Have pairs of students create or bring in their own workplace texts (e.g., work schedules or written instructions) and "white out" important words. Then they can trade these self-made cloze activities with others in the class. Depending on students' proficiency level, they can include a box with the missing words or information if needed.

   • Students can write descriptions of work situations, such as accidents, or job descriptions and "white out" every seventh to tenth word to create exercises for other students.

4. **Sequences** (1C, 2A, 3A): These exercises require putting steps in order and reinforce use of sequence words (*first, then, next,* etc.).

   Expansions:

   • Copy or have students copy a set of instructions (e.g., unjamming a copy machine or pumping gas at a self-serve station) on paper or cards, cut the steps into strips, and have students reorder them.

   • Do the same as above with picture directions. Then have students create a set of written directions for the pictures.

- Copy comic strips, separate each panel, and have students reassemble. Then have them explain the humor.

5. **Checking Off/Numbering/Circling**

   a. responding to information in readings, charts, or forms (4C, 14A, 17A, 17B)

   b. selecting positive or negative choices (1A, 4A, 7B, 11A, 12B, 13A, 18A, 18B)

   Expansions:

   - Students can make their own appointment calendar for one week or one month.

   - Gather or create a variety of forms (e.g., a job application, a blank check, a work order) and give oral instructions to guide students in completing the forms. You could say, *"Fill in your address," "Circle the name of the bank,"* etc. You can also have pairs or groups of students give instructions to each other.

   - Have student pairs create oral or written conversations on the topic of a lesson. They can use good or poor ways of asking or responding to requests, asking for or giving help, etc. After they perform their conversations, have others critique them by explaining why the conversations were good or poor.

6. **Tallying Numbers/Analyzing or Completing Data** (5A, 5B, 9B, 16A, 17B): These exercises focus on completing forms or charts or using information from documents or signs.

   Expansions:

   - Students can collect brochures on checking account fees or food or equipment prices and create charts to compare the information.

   - Bring in several months' worth of phone or electric bills and have students chart and compare usage and costs. They can also tally various parts of the bills to find long distance costs, kilowatt usage, etc.

   - Using real or adapted pay stubs, have students tally taxes and deductions.

   - Have students rewrite information from charts (evaluations, data) in narrative form.

7. **Converting Information** (3A, 3B, 5A, 9B, 13C, 14A, 15B, 16A, 18C): These exercises require students to translate information from one format to another (e.g., handwritten notes to charts or oral to written instructions).

   Expansions:

   - Have students take notes on tasks they do or observe at work. Then have them use the notes to explain the tasks orally or in writing.

   - Have students work in teams or small groups to describe a set of instructions and have the listeners (a) guess what is being done, or (b) take notes and write the instructions.

   - Have students find instructions that use mainly pictures (gas pumps, money-changing machines, etc.) and have them rewrite the steps in narrative form.

   - Bring in information from OSHA. Have students read it, take notes, and explain the guidelines to the class.

   - Have students give each other oral directions from school to their homes, to the library, to a store or mall, or to their workplaces. Then have the listeners write up the information.

8. **Rewriting, Completing, or Writing Sentences or Questions** (1A, 1B, 1C, 2C, 3A, 6C, 6D, 7A, 7B, 8B, 9A, 9B, 10B, 10D, 11B, 11C, 12C, 13B, 13C, 14B, 15A, 15B, 15C, 16B, 16C, 17A, 18A, 18B, 18C): These are the most open-ended exercises, in which students write or complete their own ideas on an activity topic.

   Expansions:

   - Individuals or pairs can create mini-conversations showing how the content of the unit is useful in their own workplaces. Other students can write and hand in questions about the conversations. The performers can read the questions and answer them aloud.

   - Students can role-play typical workplace conversations focusing on the particular language of a unit (e.g., asking/offering help or recording information on a phone message).

   - Have students bring in a set of instructions they use at work (written or visual). Then have them describe the information and have other students write or ask questions.